This Journal Belongs to:

_____

(Awesome Dad-to-Be)

If lost, please contact:

_____

"Making the decision to have a child is momentous. It is to decide forever to have your heart go walking around outside your body."
Elizabeth Stone

THIS JOURNAL IS MY GIFT TO YOU, MY CHILD. IT IS A KEEPSAKE THAT I HOPE YOU WILL TREASURE FOREVER.
I LOVE YOU TODAY & ALWAYS.
- DAD -

DADDY-TO-BE, HERE'S WHAT YOU CAN EXPECT IN THIS PREGNANCY JOURNAL:

This is such an exciting time in your life! Be sure to scan the whole journal right away so you know where to find everything described below, so that you can get the most out of it.

- " "The Pregnancy Journal" Pages - Weeks 4 – 41 – to record your weekly memories of the pregnancy
- Space to record when you found out about The Pregnancy and Fun Baby Predictions
- "My First Love Letter to My Baby"
- Space for listing your Baby Name Ideas
- Newborn Baby Shopping List
- Hospital Bag Checklist
- Our Baby Shower record
- Our Sonogram Photos
- Our Birth Plan
- Our Nursery Room Ideas
- My Family Tree
- Space to post monthly pregnancy photos
- The Birth Day, Baby's First Photo, & First Family Photos and much more!
- A whole section "About Daddy" to learn more about Daddy, Life Lessons, and Advice from Him

This journal is unique in that it offers dad guided questions, but it also offers dad plenty of space to write his own thoughts & ideas freely.
You will find some blank pages throughout. This is where dad can write even more memories that his child will treasure forever.

If MOM is looking for her own pregnancy journal, check this one out: https://amzn.to/3fUBGfT

Journal Prompts & Ideas to Write About

This journal conveniently gives you some space to journal about on different weeks of the pregnancy, and for the Daddy-to-be to journal his thoughts about various topics throughout. However, the journal is also set up so that you have the freedom to add your own topics relevant and important to you.

Here are some more topics ideas that you can choose from to get your creative juices flowing (you choose):

- Have you had any pets, and can you describe them?
- What are your political views?
- Do you have any favorite vacations to share?
- Is there anything you regret in your life, and why?
- What different paths have you been presented with in life, and how did you choose to take the one that led up to where you are now?
- If you could change one thing about your life, what would it be? Why?
- What sorts of sports and extra-curricular activities did you do as a child/teen?
- What was the best gift anyone ever gave you?
- Who are your parents and grandparents and what would you like your child to know about them?

List more of your ideas, that you don't want to forget, to write about in this journal:

_____

_____

_____

_____

_____

_____

_____

The
Pregnancy

WE ARE HAVING A BABY!

Date I found out: _____

How far along was the pregnancy?: _____

How I found out: _____

The Estimated Due Date:

_____

_____

_____

My reactions: _____

_____

_____

_____

Did I suspect we were pregnant?: _____

_____

_____

_____

Who I first told about the pregnancy & their reactions: _____

_____

_____

_____

What else do I remember about the day I found out that we were expecting our baby?:

_____

_____

_____

_____

_____

_____

_____

Before You Were Born

Prices of Common Items

Loaf of bread:

Can of soda/pop:

A dozen eggs:

Chocolate bar:

Gallon of milk:

Toothpaste:

Body wash:

Antiperspirant:

Average home purchase:

1-bedroom rental:

Arts & Culture

Popular movies of the year:

Popular songs of the year:

Price of a movie:

World Events

President/Prime Minister of our country:

Notable world events going on:

FUN PREDICTIONS

Tip: Create a prize for the person who guesses most accurately.

_____'s Prediction

Boy/Girl:

Date of birth:

Birth weight:

Time of birth:

Hours in labor:

Hair color:

_____'s Prediction

Boy/Girl:

Date of birth:

Birth weight:

Time of birth:

Hours in labor:

Hair color:

_____'s Prediction

Boy/Girl:

Date of birth:

Birth weight:

Time of birth:

Hours in labor:

Hair color:

_____'s Prediction

Boy/Girl:

Date of birth:

Birth weight:

Time of birth:

Hours in labor:

Hair color:

Fun Predictions

Tip: Create a prize for the person who guesses most accurately.

_____'s Prediction

Boy/Girl:

Date of birth:

Birth weight:

Time of birth:

Hours in labor:

Hair color:

_____'s Prediction

Boy/Girl:

Date of birth:

Birth weight:

Time of birth:

Hours in labor:

Hair color:

_____'s Prediction

Boy/Girl:

Date of birth:

Birth weight:

Time of birth:

Hours in labor:

Hair color:

_____'s Prediction

Boy/Girl:

Date of birth:

Birth weight:

Time of birth:

Hours in labor:

Hair color:

Baby Name Ideas

Girl's Names

Boy's Names

How we finally decided on your name:

Dad's First Love Letter to My Unborn Baby

_____
_____
_____
_____
_____
_____
_____
_____
_____
_____
_____
_____
_____
_____
_____
_____
_____
_____
_____
_____
_____
_____
_____
_____
_____
_____

What I looked like before you were born (add picture):

My age in photo:

The Pregnancy Week by Week

Date: | **Week 4**

What I want to remember most about this week:

Baby in Progress....Fun Facts

* Baby is the size of a poppy seed.
* Baby is a ball of cells that are rapidly multiplying.
* The primitive placenta is developing.

Date: | **Week 5**

What I want to remember most about this week:

Baby in Progress....Fun Facts

* Baby is the size of a sesame seed.
* Baby's tissues & organ systems begin to develop in Week 5.

Date: | **Week 6**

What I want to remember most about this week:

Baby in Progress....Fun Facts

* Baby is the size of a lentil, approx. ¼".
* The neural tube in baby's back closes, heart & other organs are developing, small arm buds appear, & eyes & ears primitively form.

The Pregnancy Week by Week

Week 7

Date:

What I want to remember most about this week:

Baby in Progress....Fun Facts
* Baby has doubled in size since last week, and is now the size of a blueberry.
* My baby's brain & head are growing, nostrils and retinas are starting to develop, leg buds appear, & the arm buds look like paddles.

Week 8

Date:

What I want to remember most about this week:

Baby in Progress....Fun Facts
* My baby is the size of a kidney bean, and over ½" long.
* Fingers and nose are forming, and the leg buds look like paddles.

Week 9

Date:

What I want to remember most about this week:

Baby in Progress....Fun Facts
* My baby is the size of a grape. The eyes are fully formed, but closed.
* Baby's eyelids form, baby's arms grow, elbows appear, & toes are developing.

The Pregnancy Week by Week

Date:

Week 10

What I want to remember most about this week:

Baby in Progress....Fun Facts
* My baby is the size of a kumquat, measures a bit over 1" from head to buttocks.
* My baby is the size of a kumquat, measures a bit over 1" from head to buttocks.

Date:

Week 11

What I want to remember most about this week:

Baby in Progress....Fun Facts
* My baby is the size of a fig, over 1.5" long, & can kick & stretch.
* Baby is inhaling & exhaling small amounts of amniotic fluid, exercising the lungs.

Date:

Week 12

What I want to remember most about this week:

Baby in Progress....Fun Facts
* My baby is the size of a lime, and is over 2" long from head to baby's butt.
* Baby's muscles are getting bigger, & baby is opening & closing his/her fingers, and kicking his/her arms and legs.

THE PREGNANCY WEEK BY WEEK

Date: _____

Week 13

Baby in Progress....Fun Facts
* My baby is the size of a pea pod, approx. 3" long, & weighs 1 oz.
* Baby's body is catching up to the growth of his head. All essential organs & body systems have developed, baby's kidneys are working, testicles & ovaries are formed, fingerprints are starting.

What I want to remember most about this week:

_____
_____
_____
_____
_____
_____
_____

Date: _____

Week 14

Baby in Progress....Fun Facts
* My baby is the size of a lemon, 3.5" long, & can make some facial expressions.
* My baby exhibits sucking reflexes, and is growing fine-like hair (lanugo) to help regulate his/her temperature.

What I want to remember most about this week:

_____
_____
_____
_____
_____
_____
_____

Date: _____

Week 15

Baby in Progress....Fun Facts
* My baby is the size of an apple, 4" long, & 2.5 oz.
* Baby's bones are hardening, muscles continue to form, & baby's closed eyes are starting to be sensitive to light.

What I want to remember most about this week:

_____
_____
_____
_____
_____
_____

The Pregnancy Week by Week

Date: _____
Week 16

What I want to remember most about this week:

Baby in Progress....Fun Facts
* My baby is the size of an avocado, 4.5 long, 3.5 oz.
* Baby's heart is pumping around 49 pints (28 L) of blood around his/her body every day!

Date: _____
Week 17

What I want to remember most about this week:

Baby in Progress....Fun Facts
* My baby is the size of a turnip, weighs 5 oz, & is 5" long.
* Baby's hearing is pretty good & can hear the parents' muffled voices & music. Your baby has his own set of distinct fingerprints.

Date: _____
Week 18

What I want to remember most about this week:

Baby in Progress....Fun Facts
* My baby is the size of a bell pepper, weighs 7 oz, & is 5.5 long.
* My baby is growing eyebrows.

The Pregnancy Week by Week

Week 19

Date:

What I want to remember most about this week:

Baby in Progress....Fun Facts
* My baby is the size of a large tomato, weighs 8.5 oz, & is 6" long.
* Hair may be beginning to grow on your baby's head, the brain is specializing, & mom may be feeling baby's movements at this point.

Week 20

Date:

What I want to remember most about this week:

Baby in Progress....Fun Facts
* My baby is the size of a banana, & is 6.5" from head to butt or 10" to the heels.
* This is the half point of the pregnancy! My baby is moving a lot within the womb now.

Week 21

Date:

What I want to remember most about this week:

Baby in Progress....Fun Facts
* My baby is 10.5" long (like a carrot), & weighs approximately 12 oz.
* If the mom is feeling the baby's movements, she will begin to recognize periods of wakefulness and sleeping. Baby's eyes move rapidly under the eyelids.

THE PREGNANCY WEEK BY WEEK

Week 22

Date:

What I want to remember most about this week:

Baby in Progress....Fun Facts
* My baby is the size of a spaghetti squash, weighs 1 lb, & is 11" long from head to butt.
* My baby's fingernails are clearly visible. Meconium (which will be baby's first poop) is developing in the bowels.

Week 23

Date:

What I want to remember most about this week:

Baby in Progress....Fun Facts
* My baby is the size of a large mango.
* My baby's hearing is improving to hear other sounds outside of the womb.

Week 24

Date:

What I want to remember most about this week:

Baby in Progress....Fun Facts
* My baby is about 12" (30 cm) long, & weighs 1 ¼ lb.
* My baby is considered possibly "viable" if he is born now, but really needs more time to grow & maximize the chances for survival outside the womb. My baby makes facial expressions.

THE PREGNANCY WEEK BY WEEK

Date: _____ **Week 25**

Baby in Progress....Fun Facts
* My baby is the size of a rutabaga. It is about 13.5" in length, & 1 ½ lb.
* My baby is putting on more fat in preparation for birth.

What I want to remember most about this week:

_____
_____
_____
_____
_____
_____
_____

Date: _____ **Week 26**

Baby in Progress....Fun Facts
* My baby is 14" long, 1 & 2/3 lb.
* My baby can likely recognize mom's voice & my voice too. Baby's tastebuds are developed. The lungs continue to develop.

What I want to remember most about this week:

_____
_____
_____
_____
_____
_____
_____

Date: _____ **Week 27**

Baby in Progress....Fun Facts
* My baby is the size of a cauliflower, is 14.5 long, & 2 lb in weight.
* Mom may feel when baby hiccups. My baby is also experiencing more regular patterns of sleep and wakefulness, which mom may start to notice.

What I want to remember most about this week:

_____
_____
_____
_____
_____
_____
_____

THE PREGNANCY WEEK BY WEEK

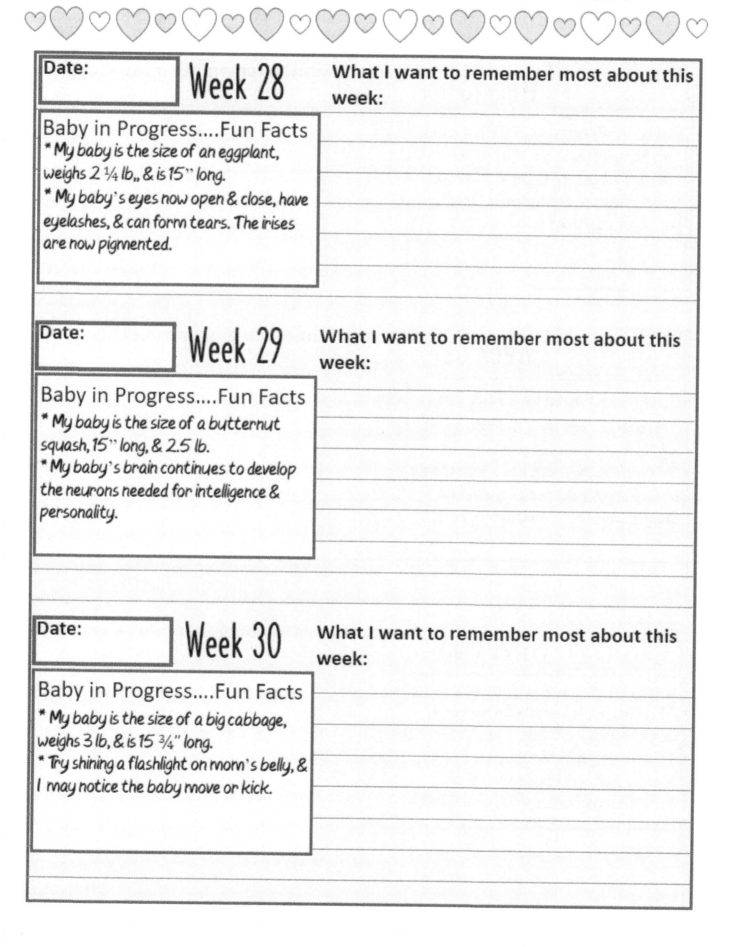

Date: _____

Week 28

What I want to remember most about this week:

Baby in Progress....Fun Facts
* My baby is the size of an eggplant, weighs 2 ¼ lb,, & is 15" long.
* My baby's eyes now open & close, have eyelashes, & can form tears. The irises are now pigmented.

Date: _____

Week 29

What I want to remember most about this week:

Baby in Progress....Fun Facts
* My baby is the size of a butternut squash, 15" long, & 2.5 lb.
* My baby's brain continues to develop the neurons needed for intelligence & personality.

Date: _____

Week 30

What I want to remember most about this week:

Baby in Progress....Fun Facts
* My baby is the size of a big cabbage, weighs 3 lb, & is 15 ¾" long.
* Try shining a flashlight on mom's belly, & I may notice the baby move or kick.

THE PREGNANCY WEEK BY WEEK

Date: _____

Week 31

Baby in Progress....Fun Facts
* My baby is the weight of a coconut.
* My baby is getting longer & bigger, so he/she takes on the curled-up, fetal position in utero until birth now.

What I want to remember most about this week:

_____
_____
_____
_____
_____
_____

Date: _____

Week 32

Baby in Progress....Fun Facts
* My baby is 16 ¾" long, & weighs approx. 3 ¾ lb..
* If born now, my baby has a good chance of surviving & being healthy, although baby's lungs aren't fully developed yet.

What I want to remember most about this week:

_____
_____
_____
_____
_____
_____

Date: _____

Week 33

Baby in Progress....Fun Facts
* My baby is the weight of a pineapple, weighs 4 lb, & is 17" long.
* Mom may notice that baby's activity level & responses are dependent on mom's own actions, such as whether she has just eaten or she's in a noisy environment.

What I want to remember most about this week:

_____
_____
_____
_____
_____
_____

THE PREGNANCY WEEK BY WEEK

Date: _____

Week 34

What I want to remember most about this week:

Baby in Progress....Fun Facts
* My baby is 18" long, & 4 ¾ lb.
* This is a great time to sing lullabies to baby, as baby is more likely to recognize them after birth.

Date: _____

Week 35

What I want to remember most about this week:

Baby in Progress....Fun Facts
* My baby is the weight of a large honeydew melon at 5 ¼ lb.
* The amniotic fluid surrounding baby is decreasing. 97% of babies are head-down at this point, in preparation for the birth.

Date: _____

Week 36

What I want to remember most about this week:

Baby in Progress....Fun Facts
* My baby is 18.5" long, & weighs close to 6 lb.
* Baby is shedding the lanugo hair & vernix caseosa (white waxy substance) this week. Baby's sucking is fully developed now.

The Pregnancy Week by Week

Week 37

Date:

What I want to remember most about this week:

Baby in Progress....Fun Facts
* My baby is approximately 19" long, & 6 1/3 lb.
* Mom passes antibodies to baby through the umbilical cord. Baby's grasp is improving, ready to grasp my fingers (and heart) when born.

Week 38

Date:

What I want to remember most about this week:

Baby in Progress....Fun Facts
* My baby weighs about 7 lb, & is 19.5" long.
* Baby continues to improve his/her breathing, circulation, & digestion.

Week 39

Date:

What I want to remember most about this week:

Baby in Progress....Fun Facts
* My baby is the weight of a watermelon, around 7 lb.
* If mom hasn't given birth yet, baby is ready to meet us any day now!

The Pregnancy Week by Week

Date: _____

Week 40

What I want to remember most about this week:

Baby in Progress....Fun Facts
* My baby is the size of a pumpkin, weighs approx. 7.5 lb, & 20" long.
* My baby will be born with many natural reflexes necessary for survival (rooting for the nipple, suckling, etc.)

Date: _____

Week 41

What I want to remember most about this week:

Baby in Progress....Fun Facts
* It should be any time now! Enjoy the last few days of the pregnancy.

THE GREATEST GIFTS YOU CAN GIVE YOUR CHILDREN ARE THE ROOTS OF RESPONSIBILITY AND THE WINGS OF INDEPENDENCE." —DENIS WAITLEY

Our Pregnancy Photo Gallery
1st Month

Date of Photo:

2nd Month

Date of Photo:

Use these pages to post pictures of the Mommy's belly or of pregnant Mommy and Daddy-to-be together.

Our Pregnancy Photo Gallery 3rd Month

Date of Photo:

4th Month

Date of Photo:

Our Pregnancy Photo Gallery 5th Month

Date of Photo:

6th Month

Date of Photo:

Our Pregnancy Photo Gallery 7th Month

Date of Photo:

8th Month

Date of Photo:

Our Pregnancy Photo Gallery 9th Month

Date of Photo:

Baby's 1st Photo

Your first breath took mine away.

THE PREGNANCY

What I did to prepare for your birth .....

_____
_____
_____
_____
_____
_____
_____
_____
_____
_____
_____
_____
_____
_____
_____
_____
_____

"ANY MAN CAN BE A FATHER, BUT IT TAKES SOMEONE SPECIAL TO BE A DADDY." ANNE GEDDES

THE PREGNANCY

My memories of seeing you on ultrasound for the first time, hearing your heart beat, seeing you move in mommy's tummy etc. …..

_____
_____
_____
_____
_____
_____
_____
_____
_____
_____
_____
_____
_____
_____
_____
_____
_____
_____

WE LOVED YOU BEFORE YOU WERE BORN, LITTLE ONE.

THE PREGNANCY

My favorite memories of the pregnancy include .....

_____

_____

_____

_____

_____

_____

_____

_____

_____

_____

_____

_____

_____

_____

_____

_____

_____

Nursery Room Ideas

Favorite website examples: _____

_____

_____

_____

_____

_____

Color scheme & theme ideas: _____

_____

_____

_____

_____

_____

_____

Draw out the layout, or add more notes:

Jack & Jill Baby Shower

Friends & family who attended:

Games we played:

Baby Shower Photo:

Our Favorite Memories of the Day:

More memorable details of our shower, including gifts received, or photos, etc.

Newborn Baby Shopping Checklist

TIP: Keep in mind that baby grows quickly so don't buy too many clothes or diapers of the same size before baby is born. Don't forget to sign up for prenatal classes and Baby CPR classes.

⭐ Clothing

- ☐ Onesies
- ☐ Sleepwear
- ☐ Undershirts
- ☐ Socks
- ☐ Slippers
- ☐ Pants or shorts
- ☐ Shirts
- ☐ Dresses
- ☐ Scratch prevention mittens
- ☐ Baby hat
- ☐ Sweaters and jackets for babies born in cool weather
- ☐ Snowsuit & mitts for baby born in winter

⭐ Sleeping

- ☐ Crib & mattress
- ☐ Sheets for crib
- ☐ Baby monitor
- ☐ Swaddling blankets
- ☐ Baby sling
- ☐
- ☐

⭐ Bathing

- ☐ Baby wash cloths
- ☐ Baby hooded towels
- ☐ Soft-bristled baby brush
- ☐ Baby body wash/shampoo
- ☐ Baby lotion
- ☐ Baby bathtub
- ☐
- ☐
- ☐

⭐ Diapering

- ☐ Diaper rash ointment
- ☐ Diaper pad &/or change table
- ☐ Baby wipes
- ☐ Diapers
- ☐ Diaper pail
- ☐ Diaper bag
- ☐
- ☐
- ☐
- ☐

⭐ Feeding

- ☐ Formula
- ☐ Baby bottles, bottle liners, bottle brush
- ☐ Burp cloths & receiving blankets
- ☐ Bibs
- ☐ High chair
- ☐
- ☐
- ☐

⭐ Miscellaneous

- ☐ Baby laundry detergent
- ☐ Infant car seat
- ☐ Stroller
- ☐ Baby thermometer
- ☐ Mobile for crib
- ☐ Rocking chair
- ☐ Night light
- ☐ Nasal bulb syringe
- ☐ Nail scissors
- ☐ Pacifiers
- ☐ Baby swing

Maternity Hospital Bag Checklist

⭐ For Mom

- [ ] Medical cards & insurance documents
- [ ] Birth plan
- [ ] Lip balm
- [ ] Maternity or loose-fitting pants & top
- [ ] Socks & Slippers
- [ ] Nightgown & robe
- [ ] Nursing pillow
- [ ] Massage oil or lotion
- [ ] Panties
- [ ] Nursing bras
- [ ] Nipple cream
- [ ] Toothbrush, toothpaste, & floss
- [ ] Hair brush
- [ ] Shampoo & conditioner
- [ ] Skin care & cosmetics
- [ ] Sheets for crib
- [ ] Deodorant/antiperspirants
- [ ] Glasses, contacts, solution
- [ ]
- [ ]
- [ ]

⭐ For Dad

- [ ] Snacks & water
- [ ] Phone, camera, video camera, & chargers
- [ ] Glasses & contact lens case
- [ ] Toothbrush & toothpaste
- [ ] Deodorant
- [ ] Change of clothes
- [ ] Book
- [ ] Money/credit card
- [ ]
- [ ]
- [ ]
- [ ]
- [ ]

⭐ For Baby

- [ ] Nightgown
- [ ] Sleepers
- [ ] Car seat
- [ ] Going-home outfit
- [ ] Socks & slippers
- [ ] Outerwear appropriate for the season
- [ ] Receiving blankets
- [ ] Pacifier
- [ ]
- [ ]
- [ ]
- [ ]
- [ ]

Important Pre-Birth Questions

Do we want a midwife or an obstetrician for the birth?

What values are important to us when choosing our midwife or obstetrician (i.e. belief in natural process, etc.)?

Is cord blood banking something we want to consider, and if so, where can we learn more?

If we have a boy, what are our thoughts on circumcision, and the risks and benefits?

Post more of our questions below:

Our Birth Plan

Who we want present at the birth: _____
_____
_____

Mom's preferences for pain control: _____
_____
_____
_____

Our agreed preferences re: medical interventions during labor: _____
_____
_____

Our agreed preferences for medical interventions during _____
delivery: _____
_____
_____

Who will cut the umbilical cord: _____

How we plan to feed our baby after birth: _____
_____

Most important issues to us: _____
_____
_____
_____

Other: _____
_____
_____
_____
_____

Our Sonogram Photos

Insert your own topic here

THE BIRTH

The Birth

Baby's Full Name:_____

Welcome to the World!

BORN ON

AT

WEIGHING & MEASURING

POUNDS

INCHES

SOME OF BABY'S FIRST PHOTOS

Trim photo to size
and place here

Trim photo to size
and place here

MORE DETAILS OF THE DAY YOU WERE BORN:

Our First Family Photos

"It is a smile of a baby that makes life worth living."
Debasish Mridha

PHOTOS OF BABY AND DADDY

GREAT THINGS COME IN SMALL PACKAGES.

THE BIRTH

My thoughts and emotions when you entered the world, and I first met you …..

_____

_____

_____

_____

_____

_____

_____

_____

_____

_____

_____

_____

_____

_____

_____

_____

_____

_____

_____

"A CHILD REACHES FOR YOUR HAND,
AND TOUCHES YOUR HEART."
AUTHOR UNKNOWN

The birth

Insert your own topic here

_____

_____

_____

_____

_____

_____

_____

_____

_____

_____

_____

_____

_____

_____

_____

_____

_____

ABOUT DADDY

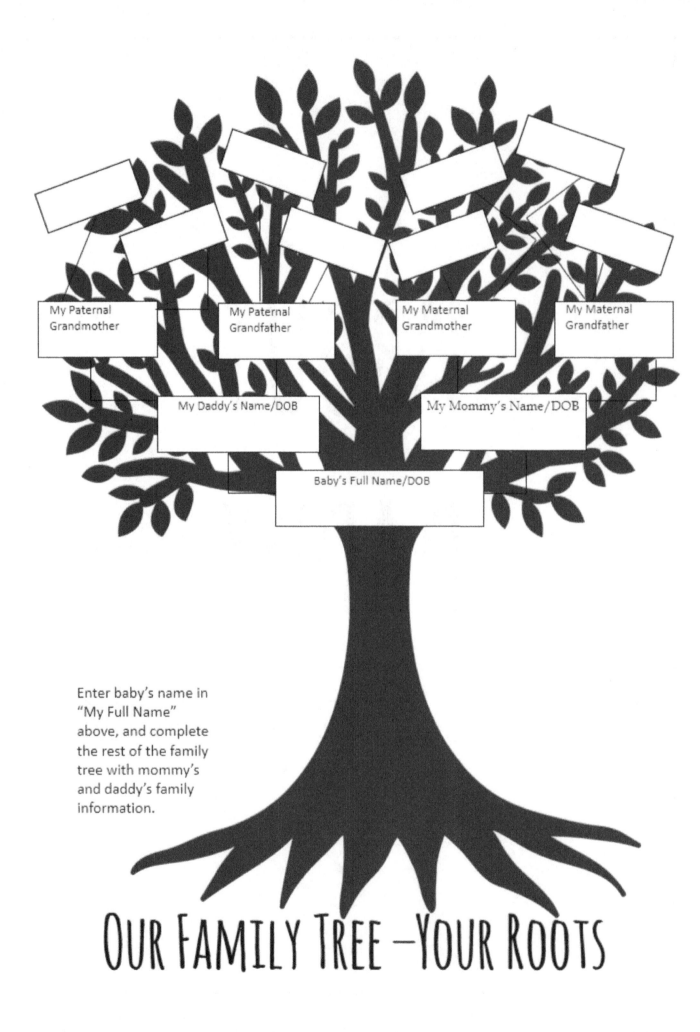

My Paternal Grandmother

My Paternal Grandfather

My Maternal Grandmother

My Maternal Grandfather

My Daddy's Name/DOB

My Mommy's Name/DOB

Baby's Full Name/DOB

Enter baby's name in "My Full Name" above, and complete the rest of the family tree with mommy's and daddy's family information.

OUR FAMILY TREE — YOUR ROOTS

Create your own family tree from scratch if you need to represent divorces or deaths, and resulting remarriages that may have occurred in your family.

Baby's full name/DOB

Daddy's Early Years

My given names: _____

Date of Birth: _____ @ City/Town: _____

State/Province: _____ Country: _____

Time of day and my weight when I was born:

_____

The reason my parents gave me my name:

_____

_____

Names, DOB of My Parents & Birth City/Country:

_____

_____

My Maternal Grandparents & DOB & Birth City/Country:

_____

_____

My Paternal Grandparents & DOB & Birth City/Country:

_____

_____

* Include dates deceased, when applicable.

Daddy's Early Years

Interesting events happening the day/year of my birth:
(local storm, who was President/PM, news stories, etc.)

_____

_____

_____

_____

_____

_____

_____

Below is a picture of me as a young child (or use it as
space to write more):

Daddy's Early Years

Use this space for any photos you have of yourself as a baby, your home, your parents, etc., &/or for more space to write your own ideas.

Daddy's Early Years

My First Memories as a Young Child:

_____

_____

_____

_____

_____

_____

_____

_____

_____

_____

_____

_____

_____

_____

_____

_____

_____

_____

_____

_____

_____

_____

"THERE ARE TWO LASTING BEQUESTS WE CAN GIVE OUR CHILDREN. ONE IS ROOTS. THE OTHER IS WINGS." HODDING CARTER JR.

Daddy's Early Years

My favorite activities that I did/toys I played with when I was a young child:

_____

_____

_____

_____

_____

_____

_____

_____

_____

_____

_____

_____

_____

_____

_____

_____

_____

_____

"THE AMAZING THING ABOUT BECOMING A PARENT IS THAT YOU WILL NEVER AGAIN BE YOUR OWN FIRST PRIORITY." OLIVIA WILDE

Daddy's Early Years

What life was like for me as a child compared to what life is like for children today:

_____

_____

_____

_____

_____

_____

_____

_____

_____

_____

_____

_____

_____

_____

_____

_____

_____

_____

_____

HOME IS WHERE THE
FAMILY IS.

Daddy's Early Years

Where I grew up, went to school, etc. .....

_____

_____

_____

_____

_____

_____

_____

_____

_____

_____

_____

_____

_____

_____

_____

_____

_____

_____

_____

 Sigmund Freud "I cannot think of any need in childhood as strong as the need for a father's protection."

Daddy's Early Years

My earliest and best childhood memories include .....

_____

_____

_____

_____

_____

_____

_____

_____

_____

_____

_____

_____

_____

_____

_____

_____

_____

_____

_____

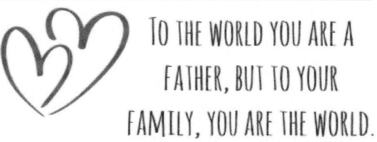 TO THE WORLD YOU ARE A FATHER, BUT TO YOUR FAMILY, YOU ARE THE WORLD.

Daddy's Early Years

This is what I liked to do as a kid …..

_____

_____

_____

_____

_____

_____

_____

_____

_____

_____

_____

_____

_____

_____

_____

_____

_____

Daddy's Early Years

When I was a kid, things I didn't like to do …..

_____

_____

_____

_____

_____

_____

_____

_____

_____

_____

_____

_____

_____

_____

_____

_____

_____

_____

Daddy's Early Years

Special skills I have include .....

_____

_____

_____

_____

_____

_____

_____

_____

_____

_____

_____

_____

_____

_____

_____

_____

_____

_____

_____

_____

_____

"My father gave me the greatest gift anyone could give another person, he believed in me."
Jim Valvano

Daddy's Early Years

My favorite music – songs, artists were/are …..

_____

_____

_____

_____

_____

_____

_____

_____

_____

_____

_____

_____

_____

_____

_____

_____

_____

_____

Daddy's Early Years

My favorite T.V. shows and movies were/are, because .....

_____

_____

_____

_____

_____

_____

_____

_____

_____

_____

_____

_____

_____

_____

_____

_____

_____

_____

_____

_____

Daddy's Early Years

Insert your own topic here

_____

_____

_____

_____

_____

_____

_____

_____

_____

_____

_____

_____

_____

_____

_____

_____

Daddy's Early Years

Insert your own topic here

_____

_____

_____

_____

_____

_____

_____

_____

_____

_____

_____

_____

_____

_____

_____

_____

_____

_____

Daddy's Early Years

Insert your own topic here

_____

_____

_____

_____

_____

_____

_____

_____

_____

_____

_____

_____

_____

_____

_____

_____

_____

_____

_____

Life Lessons, Hopes & Dreams

LIFE LESSONS

What you, my baby, have taught me about life so far .....

_____

_____

_____

_____

_____

_____

_____

_____

_____

_____

_____

_____

_____

_____

_____

LIFE LESSONS

No one is perfect. My strengths and weaknesses include ......and this is what I've done to adapt .....

_____

_____

_____

_____

_____

_____

_____

_____

_____

_____

_____

_____

_____

_____

_____

_____

_____

_____

_____

_____

_____

_____

"CHILDREN SEE MAGIC BECAUSE THEY LOOK FOR IT."
CHRISTOPHER MOORE

LIFE LESSONS

Something that I learned the hard way was …..

_____

_____

_____

_____

_____

_____

_____

_____

_____

_____

_____

_____

_____

_____

_____

_____

_____

_____

_____

Life lessons

The best lessons that I have learned in life include .....

_____

_____

_____

_____

_____

_____

_____

_____

_____

_____

_____

_____

_____

_____

_____

_____

_____

_____

_____

"A father is someone you can look up to, no matter how tall you grow."
Unknown author

LIFE LESSONS

People I find inspirational and the reasons why include .....

_____

_____

_____

_____

_____

_____

_____

_____

_____

_____

_____

_____

_____

_____

_____

_____

_____

_____

_____

"IF I COULD REACH UP AND HOLD A STAR FOR EVERYTIME YOU'VE MADE ME SMILE, THE ENTIRE EVENING SKY WOULD BE IN THE PALM OF MY HAND." AUTHOR UNKNOWN

LIFE LESSONS

What I want to teach you and do with you as you grow up .....

_____
_____
_____
_____
_____
_____
_____
_____
_____
_____
_____
_____
_____
_____
_____
_____
_____
_____
_____

"MY FATHER TAUGHT ME NOT TO OVERTHINK THINGS, THAT NOTHING WILL EVER BE PERFECT, SO JUST KEEP MOVING AND DO YOUR BEST." SCOTT EASTWOOD

Life lessons

What I hope you will always remember about me .....

_____
_____
_____
_____
_____
_____
_____
_____
_____
_____
_____
_____
_____
_____
_____
_____
_____
_____
_____

"While we try to teach our children all about life, our children teach us what life is all about." Angela Schwindt

Life lessons

Things that I am most proud about include .....

_____

_____

_____

_____

_____

_____

_____

_____

_____

_____

_____

_____

_____

_____

_____

_____

_____

DADDY'S WORDS OF ADVICE

The most important things in life are….and this is why….and the least important things in life are….

_____
_____
_____
_____
_____
_____
_____
_____
_____
_____
_____
_____
_____
_____
_____
_____
_____
_____
_____
_____
_____

My Best Advice (10 tips) & Hopes & Dreams for you as you grow up....

1. _____

INSERT YOUR OWN TOPIC HERE

INSERT YOUR OWN TOPIC HERE

Dad's Love Letter on your 1ST birthday

BEING A FATHER HAS
BEEN, WITHOUT A DOUBT,
MY GREATEST SOURCE OF
ACHIEVEMENT, PRIDE
AND INSPIRATION.
NAVEEN JAIN

Made in United States
North Haven, CT
15 May 2023

36605804R00050